My First 100 Words in
SPANISH and ENGLISH

Instructions:

Look at each scene, then at the pictures
picked out on the right. Read the word out loud
in English. Now try saying the word in Spanish.

**Remember: Always learn the "el," "la," "los," and "las" in
front of a noun together with the word itself.**

Turn to the center of the book and find the stickers
that match the scene. Stick them onto your page
and say the word again in Spanish. Now color
around the stickers to complete the picture.

**Try this: Cover up the words on the right
and try to remember the sticker words in Spanish.
Practice your Spanish by coming back to the book—cover
up the word and try to remember the Spanish word.**

At the back of the book are lots of extra useful
words to learn and practice.

© 2014 Alligator Publishing Limited, London, England.

Published by International Greetings USA, Atlanta, GA 30342

While we have made every effort to ensure the accuracy of the information in this book,
we cannot be held liable for any errors, omissions or inconsistencies.

Printed in India.

Wild animals
Los animales salvajes

elephant
el elefante

lion
el león

tiger
el tigre

zebra
la cebra

giraffe
la jirafa

flamingo
el flamenco

At the beach
En la playa

shell
la concha

crab
el cangrejo

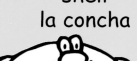

bucket
el cubo

frozen treat
la paleta

lighthouse
el faro

kite
la cometa

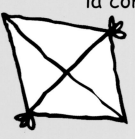

seagull
la gaviota

At the park
En el parque

pond
el estanque

duck
el pato

bush
el arbusto

slide
el tobogán

sun
el sol

bird
el pájaro

frog
la rana

Having fun
with music
Diviertiéndose
con música

guitar
la guitarra

piano
el piano

recorder
la flauta de pico

drum
el tambor

sheet music
las partituras

triangle
el triángulo

trumpet
la trompeta

Dinner time
La hora de la cena

cake
el pastel

milk
la leche

cup
la taza

jam
la mermelada

knife
el cuchillo

fork
el tenedor

spoon
la cuchara

In the bathroom
En el baño

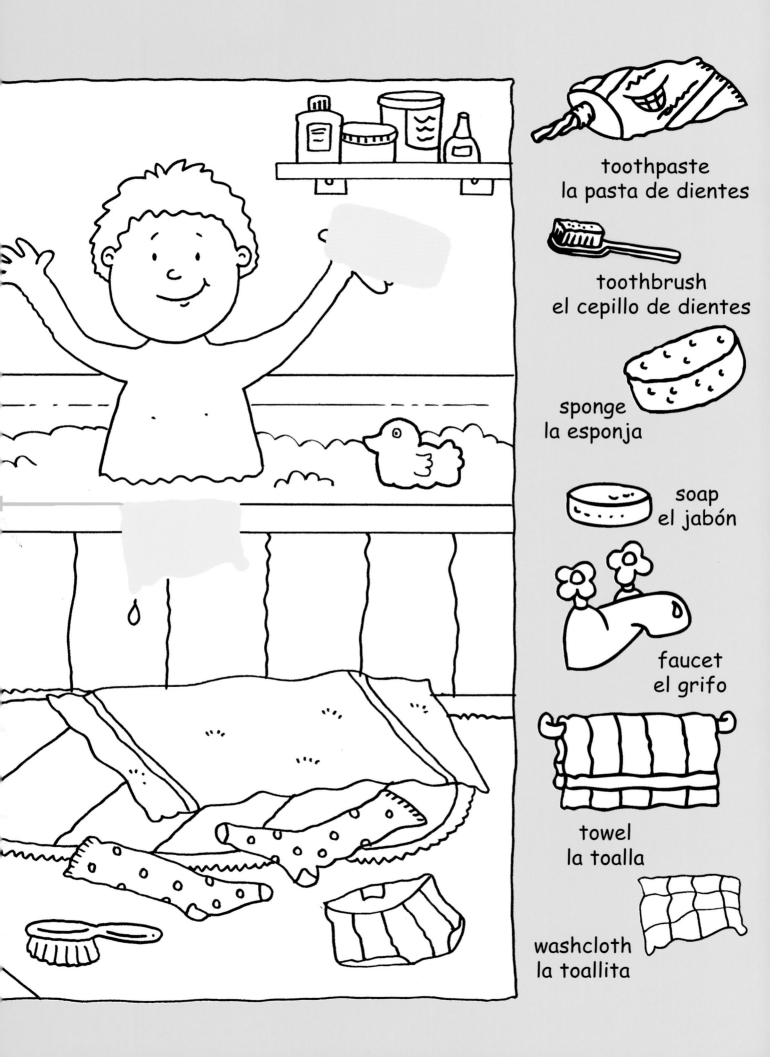

toothpaste
la pasta de dientes

toothbrush
el cepillo de dientes

sponge
la esponja

soap
el jabón

faucet
el grifo

towel
la toalla

washcloth
la toallita

My family
Mi familia

grandma
la abuela

grandpa
el abuelo

baby
el bebé

mommy
la mamá

daddy
el papá

brother
el hermano

sister
la hermana

Birthday party
La fiesta de cumpleaños

Take care when removing thin stickers as they may tear.

present
el regalo

card
la tarjeta

balloon
el globo

cake
la torta

party hat
el sombrero de fiesta

ice cream
el helado

A winter's day
Un día de invierno

scarf
la bufanda

woolly hat
el gorro de lana

snowman
el muñeco de nieve

gloves
los guantes

boots
las botas

sled
el trineo

snow
la nieve

Family room
La sala de estar

television
el televisor

sofa
el sofá

table
la mesa

newspaper
el periódico

lamp
la lámpara

picture
la foto

My favorite food
Mi comida favorita

pizza
la pizza

french fries
las papas fritas

macaroni and cheese
los macarrones
con queso

hot dogs
las salchichas

toast
la tostada

boiled egg
el huevo hervido

Pets
Las mascotas

puppy
el perrito

kitten
el gatito

rabbit
el conejo

parakeet
el perico

hamster
el hámster

goldfish
el pez de colores

Shopping
Las compras

basket
la cesta

cereal
el cereal

carrot
la zanahoria

bread
el pan

tomato
el tomate

yogurt
el yogur

fish
el pescado

The soccer game
El juego de fútbol

soccer ball
la pelota de fútbol

shorts
los pantalones cortos

shirt
la camisa

goal
el gol

referee
el árbitro

fan
el aficionado

flag
la bandera

Bedtime
La hora de acostarse

pajamas
la pijama

moon
la luna

book
el libro

pillow
la almohada

bed
la cama

slippers
las zapatillas

teddy bear
el osito de peluche

Numbers
Los números

one	uno
two	dos
three	tres
four	cuatro
five	cinco
six	seis
seven	siete
eight	ocho
nine	nueve
ten	diez

Days of the week
Los días de la semana

Monday	lunes
Tuesday	martes
Wednesday	miércoles
Thursday	jueves
Friday	viernes
Saturday	sábado
Sunday	domingo

Months of the year
Los meses del año

January	enero
February	febrero
March	marzo
April	abril
May	mayo
June	junio
July	julio
August	agosto
September	septiembre
October	octubre
November	noviembre
December	diciembre

Here are some more words for you to learn!